PR1

Landscape Assessment
for Indicative Forestry Strategies

Gareth Price
Landscape Architect
The Forestry Authority for England

WITHDRAWN

The Forestry Authority is part of the Forestry Commission

© *Crown copyright 1993*

ISBN   0 85538 318 6

FDC   911 : 903 : (420) : (429)

Keywords Forest policy, Forestry, Landscape, Land use planning

Acknowledgements

I thank South and West Region Forest Enterprise and Staffordshire County Council forestry section for implementing the project and, in particular, James Swabey and Andy Goode, respectively, for developing and carrying out much of the work and providing a great deal of helpful advice in the preparation of this document.

Due credit must also be given to Warwickshire County Council and the Countryside Commission on whose work the project was based, and also to the work undertaken for the project by Stephen Warnock, then of Land Use Consultants.

Thank you also to Brian Hibberd, Simon Bell and Judith Cheney for additional technical and editorial help.

For further information contact:

The Forestry Authority for England
Great Eastern House
Tenison Road
Cambridge
CB1 2DU

Contents

Summary

The assessment of landscape is considered in relation to developing an indicative forestry strategy. A method used successfully to assess the landscape of Staffordshire in 1991 is described with suggestions for further improvement. It is hoped that the experience gained and lessons learnt will provide useful and practical guidance to others considering similar projects.

The recommended method involves:

(1) a reconnaissance survey;

(2) a desk survey, in which the landscape is divided into basic units, or land parcels, and a three-character code based on land use, field pattern and tree cover is assigned to each; a landcover map and a landscape unit map are constructed;

(3) a field survey, in which observation in the field, using a standard character assessment sheet, allows a visual description of the units coded in the desk survey; and

(4) collation and analysis of data from the surveys.

These four stages lead to a pictorial and written description of each landscape type within the area being surveyed and to the preparation of woodland guidelines.

Résumé

L'évaluation du paysage est considérée un relation avec la mise au point d'une indication de stratégie forestière. Une méthode utilisée avec succès pour évaluer le paysage du Staffordshire en 1991 se trouve décrite et accompagnée de suggestions visant à son amélioration. On espère que l'expérience acquise et les leçons apprises fourniront des informations pratiques et utiles, capables de guider d'autres personnes désireuses d'entreprendre des projets similaires.

La méthode recommandée comprend:

(1) un levé de reconnaissance;

(2) une étude sur table, au cours de laquelle le paysage est divisé en unités de base, ou parcelles de terrain, et un code à 3 caractères est assigné à chacune suivant l'utilisation du terrain, la configuration des champs et le couvert arboré; une carte du couvert du terrain et une carte des unités de paysage sont aussi dressées;

(3) une étude sur le terrain, au cours de laquelle les observations effectuées sur le terrain à l'aide d'une fiche standard d'évaluation des caractéristiques permettent d'effectuer la description visuelle des unités codifiées lors de l'étude sur table; et. . .

(4) la collation et l'analyse des données provenant des études et du levé.

Ces quatre étapes amènent à une description écrite et en images de chaque type de paysage présent dans la zone étudiée et à la préparation de lignes directrices concernant la gestion des bois.

Zusammenfassung

Die Bewertung der Landschaft wird, in Bezug auf die Entwicklung einer angebrachten Forststrategie, betrachtet. Eine Methode, die 1991 erfolgreich zur Bewertung der Landschaft in Staffordshire benutzt wurde, wird hier beschrieben mit Anregungen für weitere Verbesserungen. Es wird erhofft, daß die hierbei gesammelten Erfahrungen sich für andere, die ähnliche Projekte erwägen, als nützlich und praktisch erweisen.

Die vorgeschlagene Methode beinhaltet:

(1) Eine Aufklärungsübersicht.

(2) Eine Schreibtischübersicht, in welcher die Landschaft in Grundeinheiten oder Landparzellen aufgeteilt wird und jeder ein dreiteiliger Schriftzeichenschlüssel zugeteilt wird, der sich auf Landnutzung, Feldmuster und Baumdeckung bezieht. Eine Landbedeckungskarte und eine Landeinheitenkarte werden angelegt.

(3) Eine Feldübersicht, in welcher die Beobachtungen vor Ort, mit Hilfe eines genormten Schriftzeichenbogens, die visuelle Beschreibung der, in der Schreibtischübersicht verschlüsselten, Landparzellen ermöglicht, und

(4) Vergleich und Analyse der in den Übersichten gesammelten Daten.

Diese vier Phasen führen zu einer bildlichen ud schriftlichen Beschreibung jedes Landschafttypes innerhalb des betroffenen Gebietes und zur Vorbereitung von Forstrichtlinien.

Introduction

In June 1991, the Forestry Commission and Staffordshire County Council embarked on a joint assessment of the landscape of the county with a view to providing the foundation for an indicative forestry strategy. The approach and the experience gained form the basis for these guidance notes.

The purpose of the guidance notes is to:

(a) give an account of the method used in a successful landscape assessment,

(b) use this example to offer practical advice and guidance to anyone undertaking a landscape assessment as part of an indicative forestry strategy,

(c) describe a method of landscape assessment that will enable a consistent approach across local authority boundaries, and

(d) provide the basis for a suggested standard format for landscape assessment, for the terminology employed and for map and descriptive presentation.

The notes are aimed at people working at the level of a County, Metropolitan District or National Park, intending to carry out a landscape assessment that could be used to produce an indicative forestry strategy. It is assumed that practitioners in such a project already possess some experience and are aware of work undertaken in Warwickshire by the County Council (1991) and the Countryside Commission (1991).

Although the method described relates specifically to the experience in Staffordshire, the approach is adaptable and can be tailored to suit the individual nature and character of the landscape in other regions of England and Wales.

It adopted the principles of defining wide regional landscape patterns, surveying by aerial photographs and map overlays and using a standard-format check sheet for field assessment.

Quite early on in the project, it became apparent that some adaptation and tailoring was required to respond to differences in the landscape between Staffordshire and Warwickshire. This publication describes how this modification was achieved. Fortunately, Staffordshire's naturally diverse landscape, which ranges from the Black Country to the Peak District, and from intensively farmed open areas to small-scale ancient landscapes, provided an excellent test of the robustness of the method and a good indication of its adaptability.

Why assess the landscape?

The landscape in England and Wales is currently under pressure as never before and there is public concern about future changes. Decision makers and land managers need good information about the landscape so that change can be steered and guided while economic activity continues. An assessment of landscape character is needed for this; it should be as objective as possible, while recognising subjectivity, and as consistent as possible over the country. Any method should also be simple and straightforward for use by a range of people.

The landscape is composed of three aspects: **the components**, e.g. landform, trees, hedges, buildings; **their physical attributes**, e.g. shape, colour, size, position; **and the way they are arranged** and the subsequent patterns they make. There is an almost infinite variation in the way in which these factors interact, so each area has its own unique character.

There is also a human response to these patterns in the landscape, a response affected by the cultural background, familiarity with the area and personal views of the observer. The presence of a vested interest in the landscape in question, such as that of a farmer or land manager, will naturally affect personal response.

Many landscapes also have historical or cultural associations, perhaps as the scene of a battle, or the location for a work of literature or painting.

The landscape is never static, it is always changing. The rate of change may be fast or slow, ranging from seasonal cycles to long-term shifts in farming practices. The capacity of the landscape to absorb far-reaching changes may vary and hence the effect of change may differ. An assessment of landscape character provides a snapshot of the landscape at a particular time and so must be viewed in the context of its continuing development.

Patterns perceived by the viewer are the result of a number of processes at work. Few landscapes have been consciously designed. Most are the result of a varying combination of natural processes and human influences changing over time. If future landscape change is to be guided, both these aspects must be encompassed.

When assessing landscape character, at whatever scale, it is important to be as objective as possible in the description of the pattern, relating the pattern to its origins, its cultural and historical associations and to the major current influences at work in it. At this stage, preferences for particular areas and value judgements have no place. The character is what it is, seen at a moment in time, subject to the continuing process of change.

Landscape assessment in relation to indicative forestry strategies

It is important, at the outset, that landscape assessment is seen as separate from indicative forestry strategy. A landscape assessment is not a forestry strategy, although in many cases it will provide a substantial basis for it. In these cases, it is important that the assessment guides the strategy and not vice versa. To this end, it is essential that a landscape assessment is dictated by the scale and character of the landscape, not at a scale dictated by the strategy.

Within lowland England and Wales there are few physical constraints on tree planting and, in many areas, the greatest influence on forest and woodland creation will be its effect on the landscape. If the Forestry Authority and others are to place confidence in an indicative forestry strategy, they must first have confidence in the landscape assessment on which many of the decisions will be made. To achieve this, it is important that the assessment method is based on sound methodology and consistent use of agreed terminology.

Indicative forestry strategies were first prepared in Scotland, led by Strathclyde Regional Council (1988). Their value for guiding woodland development became apparent immediately. These strategies were coarse in their scale of resolution, reflecting the generally large-scale nature of the Scottish landscape. They started with the major constraints to tree planting imposed by site exposure and the need to conserve existing areas of valuable seminatural vegetation. In lowland areas these are lesser constraints and landscape character is much more important. A framework and method was therefore needed that would meet the requirements of England and Wales. It had to be applicable consistently yet be flexible enough to adapt to regional variations in both landscape character and scale.

Work between landscape architects in the Forestry Commission (James Swabey of the former West England Conservancy) and those in the Forestry Section of Staffordshire County Council (Andy Goode) began in summer 1991. The approach and method drew heavily in its development on landscape assessment undertaken by the Countryside Commission (1991) and Warwickshire County Council (1991). The project also drew on the expertise gained in Warwickshire by Steven Warnock.

Guidance on indicative forestry strategies in the form of a joint circular published in 1992 between the Department of the Environment (Circular 29/92) and the Welsh Office (Circular 61/92) was a welcome step in encouraging the expansion of new woodland. Increasingly, new woodlands and forests are designed with multiple objectives in mind and their value for landscape, recreation and wildlife is seen to be as important as timber production. The Forestry Authority sees indicative forestry strategies as complementary to its own policies and grant structure, and valuable in ensuring that these objectives are correctly targeted and that the influence of more tree planting on the landscape is properly identified.

Starting with a description of landscape character provides a context and a baseline on which to measure change and to guide design (see Fig. 1).

To meet successfully the guidance issued in the joint circular, the preparation of an indicative forestry strategy should consider four key stages.

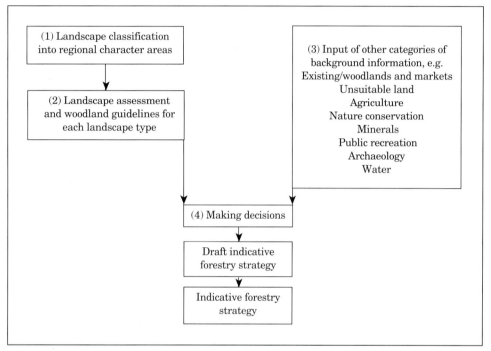

Figure 1. Suggested context of landscape assessment within an indicative forestry strategy.

(1) Landscape classification

One of the main conclusions of the Warwickshire landscape study (Warwickshire County Council 1991) was that landscape character is strongly influenced by factors that are part of a wider regional landscape pattern. Landscape classification is the identification of these wider patterns. Identified areas can be described as 'regional character areas' (Warnock & Cooper 1991) and can be defined as 'tracts of countryside where common physical, historical and ecological associations impart a sense of unity to the landscape'.

They are not vital in landscape assessment, but have proved extremely useful and help to ensure that assessments successfully cross administrative boundaries. The possibility of a nationally based regional classification is being examined by a number of agencies.

(2) Landscape assessment

A well-structured logical method of describing the landscape, which can be repeated across the country with a common terminology, is essential. This is the most important and potentially time-consuming part of developing an indicative forestry strategy.

It is perceived that in many cases the strategy alone will not provide sufficient information to guide woodland creation correctly. In these instances accompanying guidance based on landscape assessment is essential.

(3) Input of other categories of background information

This information tends to be factually based, much of it already being held by the local authority and, therefore, relatively easy to collect. Each category (see Department of the Environment & Welsh Office 1992, Appendix A, paragraph 5) recorded in map form will sit comfortably onto the landscape assessment as an overlay, enabling analysis to be made in context.

(4) Making decisions (synthesis)

After interpreting the information, strategic decisions can be made at this stage. It is obvious that the best and most accurate information is needed on which to base these decisions. The priority given to each category of background information will differ from area to area.

The Method of Landscape Assessment used in Staffordshire

Staffordshire is a predominantly rural, midland county situated a little to the north of the centre of England, with Birmingham just to the south and Stoke-on-Trent to the north. Its greatest length north to south is 56 miles and its extreme width from east to west is nearly 38 miles. The two main centres of high population density are the industrial areas based on the two great coalfields: Cannock and the Black Country to the south and the Potteries to the north. This rapid industrial and urban expansion of the eighteenth and nineteenth centuries has influenced the landscape character of the surrounding rural countryside.

The county is situated on the northernmost limit of the major division of lowland England, suggested by Dr Oliver Rackham (1986), between the 'ancient countryside' of irregular lanes, hamlets, mixed hedgerows and ancient trees and the later 'planned landscape' characterised by straight roads, villages, hawthorn hedges and large regular arable fields.

There are three well-delineated physical regions: the northern hills, the central plain and the southern plateau. In the north-east, the land rises up to the extensive millstone and limestone uplands of the Peak District. Much of this upland edge to the county is between the 120 and 250 m contours, dissected by a series of parallel rivers which flow from north-west to south-east into the River Trent. On the western side of the high hills lie the North Staffordshire coalfields, beyond which, on the western and southern edges of the coalfields, there is a border of sandstones forming a more elevated landscape.

The central plain is a low-lying tract of gently undulating landform, underlain predominantly by Keuper Marls. A series of small rivers feeds the River Trent, which rises in the north near Stoke and sweeps eastwards in a great curve.

The southern plateau protrudes like a wedge into the central plain, rising to 244 m at one point on Cannock Chase. This elevated plateau is composed of coal measures, bounded by a wide rim of Triassic sandstone, the prominent feature of Cannock Chase consisting of Sherwood Sandstones, including pebble beds.

The lowland areas are of mixed arable and pasture farmlands, largely still intact, but showing typical signs of deterioration due to removal of hedgerows and the death of hedgerow oaks. Overall, the woodland cover of Staffordshire is below the average for the UK, but equal to the average for England of approximately 6.6%, degradation being greatest in the old industrialised areas. Where the sandstones give rise to higher landforms, as on Cannock Chase, Hanchurch Hills and to the north-east, large areas of new coniferous planting form obvious features in the landscape (A. Goode 1993, unpublished).

The landscape assessment method used in 1991 involved four distinct stages (see Table 1). The tinted areas on the next few pages are comments on the method.

Stage 1: Reconnaissance survey

Although the assessors had considerable local knowledge of the area, a short reconnaissance survey, by driving around the area for 1-2 days, was carried out to establish the general character, range of variation within the landscape and the major influences. This proved helpful at a later stage when it became necessary to map and describe landcover. Where regional character areas had been identified, each was considered in turn, going through all four stages before moving onto the next.

Stage 2: Desk survey

The objective of this stage was to break down the landscape into homogeneous units, using information available from maps and aerial photographs. Choice of scale was important to establish the resolution for the strategy. Too small a scale would have meant that the assessment became too broad a brush to pick out the finer, but important, detail; while at too large a scale there was a danger that guidelines would become over-complicated, prescriptive and unwieldy. Scales varied according to the detail required, and for the desk survey several were appropriate. For the small-scale information, such as landform and geology, a scale of 1 : 50 000 was used; 1 : 25 000 or 1 : 10 000 was used for more detailed factors.

The use of larger scales is not recommended as the degree of detail becomes too great; 1 : 25 000 are the smallest-scale maps available on which field boundaries are marked.

The resolution of the survey is also determined by the overall scale of the landscape patterns, ranging from small scale in midland counties, such as Staffordshire and Warwickshire, to much larger scale for counties dominated by landform structure, such as Northumberland, or the wide open flat or rolling areas of Cambridgeshire or Norfolk. Other counties may, by their very nature, require two or more scales. The identification of regional character areas will help to make this clear.

(a) Landcover coding and mapping

Landcover can be defined as 'combinations of land use and vegetation that cover the land surface' (Countryside Commission 1991). Changes in landcover help to show how the landscape is changing.

At this stage, 1 : 25 000 Ordnance Survey Pathfinder series maps and aerial photographs were used to pick out units of similar landcover. These were coded to record land use, type of field pattern and tree cover. The coding method was borrowed from the 'Warwickshire method' (Warwickshire County Council 1991) and adapted for Staffordshire. A useful distinction in midland countrysides was between intact and fragmented field patterns; other distinctions might emerge in other areas. It was convenient to break down the area, using roads, rivers and other boundaries, into 'land parcels'.

The relevant codes will depend on the landscape in question and should be carefully chosen following the reconnaissance survey.

Table 1. Recommended procedure for landscape assessment: Summary of process

	Stage	Objective	Essential materials	Method
(1)	Reconnaisance survey	Improve general awareness and identify major influences	1:50 000 OS maps in Landranger series	Survey general range of characters and variaton over entire area by quick drive around, over 1 - 2 days
(2)	Desk survey	Landcover mapping to produce a 'land parcel' map	Aerial photographs (preferably 1:25 000, colour, but 1:10000 is acceptable) 1:25000 OS Pathfinder maps, flat 1:50000 map (reduce 1:25000 maps)	Code landcover using 3-character code and aerial photographs Code onto 1:25 000 maps Colour code onto reduced map
		Landform, drainage, geology and historical land use	1:50000 OS Landranger maps Geology survey	Trace contours onto overlay or use OS digital contouring Assimilate and simplify drift geology information onto overlay
		Overlays	Archive maps, county archaeology recorder	Analyse landcover, landform, drainage, geology and historical land use; identify; build up into units of similarity
		Landscape unit map	1:25000 OS Pathfinder series, folded	Copy 1:50000 information onto 1:25000 field survey map
(3)	Field survey	Revised landscape unit map	1:25000 OS Pathfinder series	Assess landscape in the field to revise boundaries as necessary
		Visual assessment of landscape characters	1:25000 OS Pathfinder series Blank character assessment sheets Camera	Complete character assessment sheet for each identified landscape unit Photograph samples of each area
(4)	Collation and analysis	Group similar landscape units into landscape types	1:50000 map (black and white) Regional character area map, if required	Assimilation of all previous surveys Integration with regional character areas Identify and name landscape types
		Description of landscape type and woodland guidelines	Completed character assessment sheets	Assimilation of character assessment notes Cross-reference to landscape types map
	Use in indicative forestry strategy			

11

	Code			Code for Derwent colour pencils
	X	Other land use - heath, parks, etc		(19.17)
	D	Disturbed land		(19.21)
	U	Urban land		(19.25)
	P11/P12 C11/C12	Intact ancient pasture or cropland: with small woods and copses with hedgerows, trees		(19.49)
	P13/ C13	Intact ancient with sparse/non-existent tree cover		(19.47)
	C21/P21 C22/P22 C23/P23	Ancient fragmented landscape: with strong woodland with hedgerows		(19.20)
	C31/P31 C32/P32	Planned landscape: with strong woodland with hedgerows		(19.31)
	P33	Planned pasture - weak tree cover		(19.44)
	C33	Planned cropland - weak tree cover		(19.39)
	P41/ C41	Open field pattern fragmented (planned) landscape with hedgerow trees		(19.55)
	P42/C42 P42/C42	Open fragmented planned landscape with strong woodland		(19.58)

Summary of codes:

1st digit - land use	2nd digit - field pattern	3rd digit - tree cover
C - Crop	1 - Ancient (intact)	1 - Hedgerow tree cover intact
P - Pasture	2 - Ancient (fragmented)	2 - Small woods and copses
U - Urban	3 - Planned	3 - Virtually no trees
D - Disturbed	4 - Open	
X - Other		

Figure 2. Key to types of 'land parcels' used in Staffordshire landscape assessment study, 1991.

Combinations of letters and numbers were used to assign a three-character code to each land parcel and describe the types of landcover (see Fig. 2).

Thus, a coding of P11 indicated a pasture landscape of ancient field pattern with intact hedgerow tree cover, whereas C33 was an open treeless landscape of planned crop land.

The coding was marked for each parcel on the 1:25 000 maps. The process of coding was made considerably easier and quicker by the use of coloured aerial photographs at a similar scale to the maps.

> This stage looks complicated and time consuming, but is a vital preparatory step and well worth the effort. The maps also provide a useful record of the state of the landscape at the time of the survey.

When more than one person was engaged in the exercise, cross-referencing by comparing areas coded, helped to ensure consistency.

> There is often a temptation, especially when looking at fragmented landscape, to pick out individual fields, hedgerows and even trees. Avoid this if possible. The aim is to identify overall patterns. Small-scale changes confuse the issue.

Where small woods were identified as being a composite part of the landcover, they were included within the parcel and coded as such. Larger woodlands seen to be a major element in their own right were outlined and identified separately.

Although 1:25 000 was a good scale at which to code landcover, it was too large to pick out the wider patterns (and it was also an impractical scale for a county masterplan). The coded 1:25 000 sheets were more easily handled when reduced to 1:50 000, for a more useful tool at this stage. The general patterns in the landscape were analysed using a combination of colour and cross-hatching to highlight differences and similarities in landcover. Colour selection is important and some time was taken to ensure that similar colours were used to highlight landscapes that were likely to look similar on the ground. Figure 2 illustrates the key to the coding used and Figure 3 shows examples from the final 'land parcel' map for Staffordshire.

(b) Landscape unit map

The land parcel map was used to identify patterns of similar landcover, which were subsequently described by field work. Other influences such as landform and drift geology had needed to be considered to ensure that similar areas on the plan really represented similar areas on the ground. This information was overlain onto the land parcel map and the combination of layers enabled more-refined units to be identified. This task was very important as it then provided the basis for the field survey. The resulting map was referred to as the 'landscape unit map' and, in preparation for the field exercise, it was transferred onto folded 1:25 000 OS Pathfinder maps.

> Ensure that this stage is done thoroughly and resist the urge to rush out into the field survey too early. Overlays of clear film or acetate are ideal for sieve analysis. Expert advice may be required to ensure that accurate drift geology information is available.

Figure 3a and b. Examples of part of a land parcel map prepared for Staffordshire in 1991.
Scale 1:25 000. See Fig. 2 for key to shading and coding.

Figure 3b.

Stage 3:
Field survey

The aim of the field survey is to identify influential elements and understand how they interact to create a particular landscape character.

The desk survey subdivided the landscape into basic units from factual information. The field survey was a check of what was on the ground and allowed a visual description of each subdivision.

It is important to confine the field survey to an objective description which avoids qualitative judgement as far as possible. An accurate desk survey pays dividends in saving time and resources when out in the field, by providing the surveyors with an accurate overview of landscape patterns and change against which the visual assessment can be made.

Of all the stages in the assessment, this is possibly the most crucial and, in the past, where many of the weaknesses of landscape assessments have become evident. In many cases, a major weakness was the confusion over terminology used to describe landscape. This, in turn, resulted in subjective interpretations, which are open to criticism and lack of credibility. It is not possible to eliminate subjectivity altogether, but recognition and control of it results in greater credibility. The first step towards achieving this is by the use of an agreed vocabulary. Appendix 1 provides a glossary of recommended terms.

(a) Assessment in the field

When the landscape units had been transferred on to the 1:25 000 OS Pathfinder map series, field work could commence. The scale provided a suitable resolution at which larger-scale patterns were still visible and features such as field patterns, woodlands, copses and field ponds could be identified.

The first task was to check that the boundaries shown on the map actually registered as a change in character on the ground. This was done by establishing the general 'feel' for the unit, driving along the boundaries (or as near to them as possible) and testing whether the change on the map was actually visible. If, for instance, the map showed a change from one side of a lane to the other which was not visible on the ground, the boundary line was moved. (Soft pencils and erasers were needed for this part of the exercise.) Photographs were taken to illustrate the 'typical' character of the unit.

There are considerable advantages in the field survey being carried out by two suitably trained people. Apart from the obvious practical problems of combining driving with navigating, there is much to be gained from discussion of aspects of the landscape character.

Another useful part of checking the boundaries of landscape units was that the surveyors were simultaneously accumulating information and discussing the character of the unit being assessed – the elements, differences from adjacent units, etc. This ensured that at the next step (which was writing the unit description) a clear understanding of the factors involved had already been gained.

While carrying out the survey, it is also worth remembering the question of scale. It is often easy to be misled by localised changes in character, forgetting that it is the overall patterns that are important. Occasional back reference to the landcover map is helpful in avoiding this.

(b) Visual assessment of landscape character

Once the boundary of the landscape character unit had been established, the next stage was to describe it.

The best results were achieved by completing character assessment sheets straightaway. It was helpful to find a position giving a representative view of the unit from which to write it.

The character assessment sheets were developed to provide as full a summary of the unit as possible; some further adjustment to suit regional variation may be required. An example of such a sheet is given in Table 2. The sheet comprises five sections: historical and ecological associations; landscape elements; aesthetics; brief description; and woodland guidelines. Each section is clear-cut in its definition; care was taken to ensure that, when completing the sheet, descriptions adhered to this. Failing to do so led to unnecessary repetition and/or missing key points. The section on woodland guidelines did not strictly belong to the basic assessment, but in the context of an indicative forestry strategy it saved time and repeat visits to the area.

(i) Historical and ecological associations.

Going through the checklist, all relevant elements were recorded. This began to build up a picture. Some elements were identified from observation, but most could also be picked up from the 1:25000 Pathfinder map.

(ii) Landscape elements.

Before writing the descriptions, it was helpful to identify key elements within the unit, e.g. woodlands and landform, or field pattern with fences. Once identified, these were ringed as a reminder. See Appendix 2 for examples of completed character assessment sheets.

Having identified the dominant elements, they were described, ensuring that the descriptions were concise and factual only, e.g. age, composition and condition of woodlands and hedgerows; type, size and style of settlements; type and size of water features; and size and distribution of power and road networks.

Avoid subjective comments!

(iii) Aesthetics.

Having identified and described the elements, the next step was to understand how they interrelated to create the visual character. Again, it was important to be meticulous in the descriptions and to avoid subjectivity (see Appendix 1 for a glossary of terms by which these aesthetic elements can be described).

The purpose of this section is to describe the visual appearance of the landscape, not to establish quality standards.

17

Table 2. Example of blank character assessment sheet

Landscape character assessment sheet

Sheet No.   Location: Date   Photo: Film No.
                                                 1:25 000 OS Sheet

Historical and ecological associations: are any of the following present?

Hamlets	Irregular fields	Narrow lanes	Ancient woods	Railways
Villages	Mixed hedges	Hedge banks	Parkland	Dykes
Commons	Field ponds	Bracken	Heathland	Plantations
Historic sites	Ridge and furrow	Hedgerow oaks	Scrub	Regular fields
Fords	Walled fields	Old pollards	Rough grass	Thorn hedges
Canals		Straight roads	Meres	

Landscape elements

Tree cover
      Woodlands
      Hedgerow trees

Field Pattern
      Hedgerows
      Fences
      Walls
      Dykes

Landform

Water

Habitation

Transport/power

Aesthetics

Organisation of elements (where, relationship to each other, interlock, etc)

Proportion and balance of elements (proportions of mass and space in balance – one element too dominant $1/3 \rightarrow 2/3$ etc.)

Scale of the landscape (what, controlled by, effect of mass/space on scale)

Texture/colour (notable influences, both short- and long-term)

Diversity (how much – increasing, decreasing, static; why – within landscape unit, within typical composition)

Contributors to genius loci

Degree of unity (how much in the landscape unit; how much in a typical composition; main contributors/detractors)

Visual travel (how the eye moves around the typical composition)

Brief description

Woodland guidelines

(iv) Brief description.	The brief description helped to tie the elements and the aesthetics together to give a 'pen picture' of the unit and also helped to highlight other points. It was difficult when writing the pen picture to avoid feelings and opinions showing through. The value of two surveyors showed here.
(v) Woodland guidelines.	Having gone through the check sheet, the surveyors now had a clear picture of the landscape unit.

Using this together with considered professional judgement, it is helpful to give (in rough note form at this stage) possible guidelines on the design and location of new woodlands that will be compatible with the character of the landscape.

Stage 4: Collation and analysis

The analysis stage involved collating and assimilating the accumulated data from the surveys to group together similar landscape units into landscape types.

There is no easy method for this, which involves carefully working through the character assessment sheets. The identification of matching keywords and dominant elements is a valuable opening exercise. Reference to the regional landscape classification also ensures that this grouping relates to the wider landscape patterns.

The areas identified in this way were given names which fitted their location and description. A map at a scale of 1:50 000 was used to illustrate this information (see Fig. 4 for an example).

Description of landscape type

Once the landscape types had been identified, the next step was to describe each, using the character assessment sheets.

The aim was to present a precise and succinct pictorial and written description for each landscape type. It was important that all the key contributors to the landscape character were highlighted. Care was taken, however, to avoid identifying specific areas or features. Instead, a composite, representative scene was prepared.

For this reason, a sketch is recommended in preference to photographs (see Fig. 5 for examples).

Using the woodland design guidelines

An indicative forestry strategy is intended to guide and assist the creation of new woodlands. On the basis of the description, woodland guidelines are suggested. The design guidelines provide models of how woodland can be accommodated in each landscape type according to the character. They do not contain any assumptions about the desired extent of such woodland, or specify where it should be located, except in its context within the landscape. This is the role of an indicative forestry strategy itself. There should be no coercion or obligation on owners to plant trees in particular places. However, it will be easier for an owner to obtain a grant, if the design guidance contained in the strategy is followed. Detailed design of individual proposals is also required to take into account local conditions and constraints.

It is estimated that the Staffordshire assessment took approximately 200 days to complete, including the learning process.

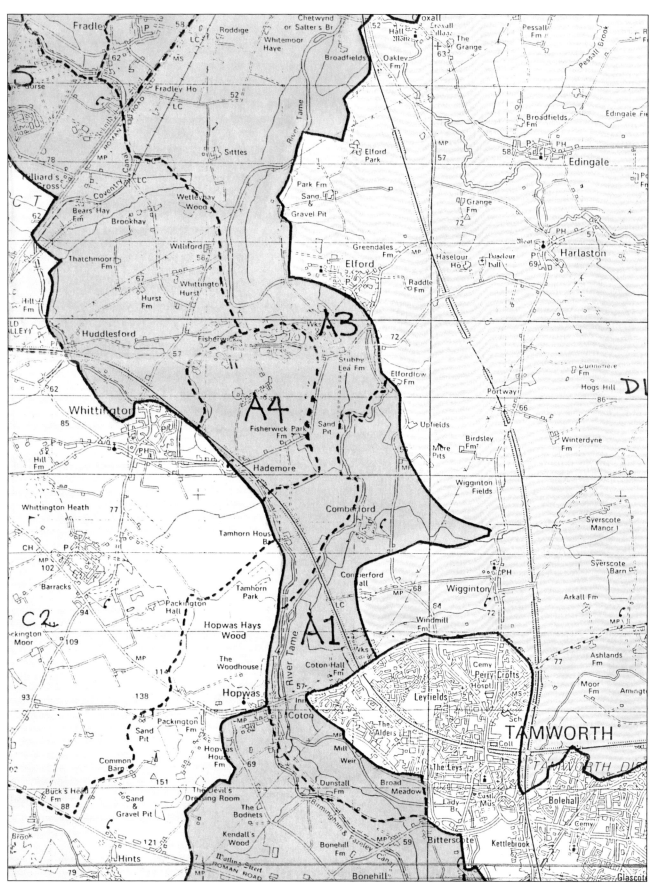

Figure 4. Example of a landscape type map prepared for Staffordshire in 1991. Scale 1:50 000.

A4 FLAT RIVER TERRACE

An area of flat intensively farmed predominantly arable land. The field
pattern tends to be large scale and regularly shaped although there are
pockets of irregulaly shaped, ancient fields. However this difference is
indistinct on the ground as the lack of landform means that views through
the landscape are controlled by how intact the hedgerows are and the
density of the tree cover. In areas where vegetable growing takes place,
hedgerows have been removed, hedgerow trees are sparse and the sense of
enclosure has been lost as the scale of the landscape increased. In the
pastural pockets the texture tends to be coarser with largely intact
hedgerows etc.

Throughout the majority of the arable areas the loss of stock control
function has led to both sculpted, gappy and overgrown thorn hedges. Trees
in these tend to be oak, ash and thorn and their density varies from
scattered to sparse. Their presence gives a filtered view through the
landscape often for 2-4 fields depth. In the few places where small
woodlands are present their edges coalesce with hedgerow trees to give a
strong sense of enclosure.

Streams and ditches reinforce this enclosure with lines of willows and
alders. The major roads and canal have a strong localised influence as the
flat landform ensures that they are very visible. The area is also served
by a widely spaced network of both straight and narrow winding lanes
servicing the scattered large C19th farmsteads. The flat topography and
varying density of hedgerows and tree cover means that views out of the
area to woodland edges in adjoining areas are important.

Figure 5a, b and c. Examples of completed sheets for description of landscape type and woodland guidelines in Staffordshire in 1991.

Woodland Guidelines

Large scale woodland plantings of field size and shape are appropriate. Care should be taken to ensure that edges have a graded profile. Mixed woodlands are appropriate but care should be taken to avoid a horizontally layered appearance.

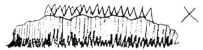

To ensure that the scale of the landscape does not change rapidly and that views through to the adjoining landscapes are respected siting of additional woodlands is important. Woodlands should not be allowed to coalesce into a continuous solid woodland screen blocking off all views through the landscape. They should generally be sited at least one field back from roads and major viewpoints. Field sized and shaped woodlands would be suitable.

VIEWS THROUGH
KEPT OPEN

VIEWPOINTS FROM ROAD

WOODS ADJACENT
TO ROAD FOR SHORT
DISTANCE ONLY.

B5 NEEDWOOD PARKLANDS

This is a wooded pastural landscape of steep slopes running down to streams which run off the Needwood Plateau. The woodland is predominantly broadleaved and principally located in valleys or on hill tops. There are areas where the woodlands visually coalesce to give a large scale forested feel. Hedgerow trees are predominantly mixed age oak with evidence of succession and the large number of them contribute strongly to the woody character of the area.

The field pattern is of both medium scale ancient and planned origins. Hedgerows are largely intact although there is evidence of some localised neglect where fences are beginning to appear. Manors with attendant parkland have a strong localised effect on the landscape. The area is well populated with hamlets and medium sized farms serviced by network of both straight and winding lanes.

In summary this is a peaceful well cared for landscape where the woodlands interlocking with both the fields and the landform are the dominant characteristics.

Figure 5b.

WOODLAND GUIDELINES – NEEDWOOD PARKLANDS

1. In areas that are already well wooded some expansion can be catered for by expanding existing hilltop and valley woods with broadleaved planting. It is important to avoid coalescence and subsequent closing off of the slopes.

2. In areas that currently have less woodland cover additional broadleaved woodlands could be sited on hilltops and in valleys. On hilltops and where the field pattern has broken down shaping should reflect landform.

3. Hedgerows and the hedgerow tree pattern are relatively intact. Any further decline should be arrested with a Hedgerow Conservation project.

4. Parklands should be treated on an individual basis. An historical survey and analysis must be carried out before any additional woodland is contemplated.

D1 OPEN ROLLING FARMLANDS [MEASE]

An area of predominantly intensively farmed arable land with a well ordered and kempt appearance. The field pattern is generally of large scale regularly shaped fields with areas of large scale ancient pattern being present one field back from the road in places. However the gently rolling landform does not allow this ancient pattern to register strongly. The hedgerows are generally closely cropped single species (thorn) becoming gappy as there is little current stock control function. Hedgerow trees are sparse and predominantly Oak and Ash with areas where the former show signs of widespread dieback. In the vales hedgerow trees coalesce to give a woodland effect. There are pockets where field sized broadleaved plantation woodlands occur which in this open landscape have a marked visual effect. The eye tends to move through this landscape easily and focuses on the many large farmsteads or the intervisible village church spires before moving along the intermediate skylines to the long views. This is a well ordered landscape of open views and quiet rural character.

WOODLAND GUIDELINES
D1 OPEN ROLLING FARMLANDS [MEASE]

Large scale woodlands of field size would be appropriate and have a visual effect much greater than their size would suggest. Where the field pattern is intact it will be appropriate to shape to this. Where it is not intact great care should be taken to shape the lower margin in very gentle curves to reflect the rolling landform.

Edge detail to achieve a graded edge is crucial

Figure 5c.

Mixed woodland would be acceptable as long as edges and skylines were well handled.

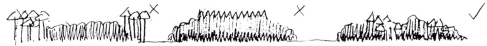

In the pockets where there are appreciable amounts of woodland care should be taken not to block off views through the landscape with planting that coalesces with that existing. In these areas the vales will be more suitable for planting than the tops of slopes and a useful device will be to extend existing woodlands. A hedgerow tree conservation project would help to link new woodlands into the wider landscape.

Conclusion and Discussion of the Method

There are numerous additional benefits associated with a landscape assessment. It can provide the foundation for any number of rural strategies, such as for housing, roads and minerals. The assessment can be used as a county-wide landscape inventory to which planners can refer and which can be used to support the cases for or against particular forms of development.

The key to successful landscape assessment relies in the use of a consistent approach and terminology. It is hoped that the method described here and the suggested modifications provide the basis for this. It is strongly recommended that they are substantiated by further training. It is hoped that the experience and lessons learnt will provide useful and practical guidance to others who are considering similar projects.

Establishing a feel for the main landscape character early on proved important in successfully developing the system.

The use of a thorough desk survey was invaluable in providing data for field work. The objective was to analyse aerial photographs, drift geology, landform and historical information in a structured and logical way, providing the assessors with a clear picture of areas of similar landscape character. One lesson learnt was not to hurry into the field survey work. Much time could have been wasted out in the field if landscape character boundaries had not been clearly or accurately defined.

Field survey work had to ensure that areas identified in the desk study were actually seen as a visible change in the landscape. The duration of field work depended on the quality of the desk study and the scale and complexity of the landscape.

Once the landscape units had been identified, the next step involved describing them. Consistency was essential, and to achieve it a standard survey check sheet was used. This ensured that all the relevant information was recorded in a regular and understandable order each time.

Such survey sheets need to be tailored to suit local circumstances, but they should include the following factors:

(a) Features present within the unit, e.g. historic artefacts, narrow lanes and stone walls. This helped to develop the assessor's understanding and proves helpful in providing keywords when it comes to synthesising the information later.

(b) Landscape elements, e.g. woodlands, landform and field patterns. These were the elements that could effect the character of an area. A brief description was given for each with an indication of the dominant ones.

(c) Aesthetics, e.g. scale, visual travel, texture and colour. The analysis not only identified the elements, but also described their relationship to each other and the effect they had on what was seen. The aim was to be as objective as possible and to avoid qualitative judgements. To ensure that subjectivity was minimised, it was essential that the descriptions were based on consistent use and understanding of the terminology. The woodland design guidelines of the Forestry Authority (1989, 1991, 1992) describe and explain many of the principles and illustrate how they may be applied to woodland design.

(d) Brief description. This helped tie all the information together and provide a 'pen picture' of the area.

(e) Woodland guidelines. To save time it was helpful to note initial thoughts on woodland design requirements before leaving the area. This also proved helpful in synthesising information later.

Having completed the field work, the final task was identifying the landscape types by grouping together similar areas identified in the survey sheets and describing each. There is no easy method for this, which involves carefully working through the survey sheets. The identification of matching keywords and dominant elements is a valuable opening exercise.

The goal in the Staffordshire study was to produce a county map identifying the landscape types (a scale of 1:50000 was the most appropriate for Staffordshire); and a description for each type, comprising a sketch of a typical view within the area, a brief, but concise, written description of the elements and features that influenced that character and notes on guidance for woodland design. Care was needed to ensure that the guidelines did not become prescriptive. They could not contain assumptions on the desired extent of woodland or specify where it should be located, except in its context within the landscape. There was to be no coercion or obligation on owners to plant trees in particular places. However, woodland schemes will be facilitated if guided by the assessment.

Despite the pressures on resources, there is considerable benefit to carrying out the work in-house. There is great value in local officers gaining the depth of understanding which is only possible through carrying out the survey. This should ultimately show itself in the quality of work and in the confidence that can be placed in the subsequent indicative forestry strategy.

References

Bell, S. (1993). *Elements of visual design in the landscape.* E. & F.N. Spon, London.

Countryside Commission (1991). *Assessment and conservation of landscape character.* CCP 332. Countryside Commission, Cheltenham.

Department of the Environment & Welsh Office (1992). *Indicative forestry strategies.* Joint Circular 29/92 and 61/92, respectively. HMSO.

Forestry Authority, The (1989). *Forest landscape design guidelines.* HMSO.

Forestry Authority, The (1991). *Community woodland design guidelines.* HMSO.

Forestry Authority, The (1992). *Lowland landscape design guidelines.* HMSO.

Rackham, O. (1986). *The history of the countryside.* Dent, London.

Strathclyde Regional Council (1988). *Forestry strategy for Strathclyde.*

Warnock, S. & Cooper, A. (1991). *A regional landscape classification for the Midlands - a report to the Countryside Commission.* HMSO.

Warwickshire County Council (1991). *Arden landscape guidelines.* Warwickshire County Council, Planning and Transportation Department.

Appendix 1

Glossary of terms used
in landscape assessment

Descriptive vocabulary

At the stage of field assessment of landscape units prior to defining landscape types, the analysis moves into character description and away from map-based information of a purely factual nature. A survey sheet is usually compiled to record the information for each unit. It is at this stage that subjectivity and personal preference are likely to creep in unless rigorous adherence to standard terminology is maintained. In essence, the outcome of the field survey is a record of the key features of the patterns seen.

Experience in the Forestry Commission has shown that there are sets of discrete factors to be analysed in a logical order. This analysis, while used at this stage to determine landscape character, can also be valuable for informing subsequent strategies and design.

Of the range of factors listed by Bell (1993) not all are relevant to this kind of assessment in every place. The assessment should begin by identifying the basic elements in the landscape. Then their individual visual characteristics can be described using the following terms. Going through each is a useful discipline for the definitive work picture of each landscape type.

Balance and proportion

The proportions of different elements influence the patterns. Criteria such as $1/3$ to $2/3$ relationship of proportion (rule of thirds) can be used to assess how well balanced the landscape is in aesthetic terms. This is the assessment in the view, not taken from a plan. This should also be considered in relation to temporal effects: the proportions may change with the addition or loss of elements.

Continuity

The degree of continuity apparent in the pattern can determine the unity of the character. There may be minor variations in an area, yet the overall sense of continuity may be retained.

Density patterns

Texture or density of tree cover may vary from place to place, possibly in a defined way related to landform, soil, etc.

Diversity

This needs to be assessed in two ways. Firstly, within the boundaries of the landscape type, the minor variations of the landscape should be assessed to determine, overall, how uniform or diverse the landscape is. Secondly, the diversity of a typical composition can be evaluated. However, be wary of a landscape with a lot of elements, which is dominated by one element to the extent that it becomes fairly uniform. The time factor should be borne in mind. Is the degree of diversity increasing or decreasing?

Effect of time	The assessment is a snapshot of the landscape at one time, so any changes taking place and their likely trends need to be recorded.
Enclosure	Where elements are arranged so that they enclose space, this has an effect on the overall composition, so that the space and mass become as one. It also has a great effect on scale, the interaction between the height of the enclosing elements and the distance between them.
Genius loci	This is all about the identification of a sense of place and is more closely focused than landscape character. The dominant elements listed on the character assessment sheet refer to Table 2 and give a strong initial impression, but so do unusual or localised features. Some elements contribute negatively. As this is potentially the most subjective attribute, there should be discussion between surveyors on this aspect.
Interval between elements	This may be regular or irregular and has a marked effect on certain landscapes, e.g. trees in hedgerows, field boundaries.
Landscape textures	These vary according to scale, but can be defined in relative terms as coarse, intermediate or fine. They are determined by crops, tree cover, size of trees, species, size of fields and so on. Texture is an important contributor to design unity and diversity and is susceptible to change by addition or loss of elements.
Nearness	Are elements close enough to be read as a group, or are they more widely scattered? The apparent coalescence of trees and woods has a marked effect on the scale of the landscape and its proportions.
Position	This describes where elements are located in the landscape, e.g. on hill tops or in valley bottoms. This may relate to physical or other factors, such as soil, drainage and communications.
Rhythms	These may occur in the landscape as a result of repetition of similar elements at repeated or related intervals. Landform and streams may contribute, imparting strong character and contributing to the unity.
Scale	The overall scale of the landscape type must be assessed once the factors that define it have been established. These include the degree of enclosure by landform or woodland and the main positions from which the landscape is viewed; scale increases with elevation and distance. It is important not to be confused by a landscape that is essentially large scale yet contains small-scale elements, i.e. the pattern may be small scale, yet the landscape is large scale. Relate back to balance, proportion enclosure and interlock to help determine the important factors and the degree of scale.
Shapes and forms	Describe the shapes of fields, woods and linear features of landform, e.g. rectangular, curvilinear, rounded, flat. This is important in defining ancient or planned landscapes. Shapes and forms can be picked out quickly, often on very slight evidence.

Unity	The other terms should help towards an understanding of how unified the pattern is. The repetition of similar elements, the balance and proportion degree of enclosure and interlock all contribute. This aspect should also be considered in the context of the regional landscape area. The degree to which contrasting elements disrupt the composition must also be considered in the context of the type as a whole, e.g. a quarry or big prairie farm in the middle of an otherwise strongly continuous pattern.
Visual travel	This is an assessment of how a composition is perceived. It is related to landform through visual force and to the pattern of spaces, e.g. the open spaces between wooded areas. This can lead to some parts of the landscape being more dominant than others.

Survey sheet   Character assessment

Sheet: Location: Date: Photo: ACM. No.
                                 + 25000
                                 O.S. SHEET

Historical and ecological associations are any of the following present?

~~Hamlets~~   ~~Irregular fields~~   ~~Narrow lanes~~   Ancient woods   Railways
Villages   ~~Mixed hedges~~   ~~Hedge banks~~   ~~Parkland~~   Dykes
Commons   ~~Field ponds~~   ~~Bracken~~   ~~Heathland~~   ~~Plantations~~
~~Historic sites~~ Ridge and furrow   ~~Hedgerow oaks~~   ~~Scrub~~   ~~Regular fields~~
Fords   ~~Walled fields~~   Old pollards   ~~Rough grass~~ ~~Thorn hedges~~
~~Canals~~-feeder   Straight roads   Meres

LANDSCAPE ELEMENTS

TREE COVER — WOODLANDS — Large area of plantation woodland and occasional small conifer/broadleaf plantations – All woods follow valley bottoms.

— HEDGEROW TREES — Overgrown thorn, oaks, sycamore, ash beech holly, alder along streams.

FIELD PATTERN — HEDGEROWS — Generally unkempt/overgrown. Quite gappy in places but pattern is intact.

— FENCES — Introduced for stock control where hedges have deteriorated.

— WALLS — Drystone walls (- assoc. with fencing) low, poor condition.

— DYKES — N/A

LANDFORM — Series of steeply sloping incised stream valleys within rolling valley landform. Obvious mill stone ridge with large exposed stones on tops and heathy character eg Wicken Stones.

WATER — Reservoir and associated woodlands and small streams in main and side valleys. (Head of Trent).

HABITATION — Scattered small farms and renovated houses – predom. stone built. Evidence of neglect in areas.

TRANSPORT/POWER — Powerlines on southern edge. Lots of small lanes crossing valley from ridge to ridge.

AESTHETICS

ORGANISATION OF ELEMENTS [WHERE, RELATIONSHIP TO EACH OTHER, INTERLOCK ETC]
Strong landform superimposed by strongish landcovers of overgrown hedges, hedgerow trees and woodlands in valleys. Landform shows up all landcover features. Stones and heathland tops of ridges highlighted. No apparent logic to position of h'rows vis walls.

PROPORTION & BALANCE OF ELEMENTS [PROPORTIONS OF MASS AND SPACE IN BALANCE - ONE ELEMENT TOO DOMINANT - $\frac{1}{3} \rightarrow \frac{2}{3}$ ETC]
Landform dominant but hedges and trees still v. strong features and reduce the effect of landform to a degree – Highlights main patterns.

SCALE OF THE LANDSCAPE [WHAT, CONTROLLED BY, EFFECT OF MASS/SPACE ON SCALE]
V. small → medium scale – controlled by landform (large and small scale) and by trees and hedgerows.

An example of a completed character assessment sheet used in the Staffordshire study in 1991.

TEXTURE / COLOUR [NOTABLE INFLUENCES BOTH SHORT AND LONG TERM]
Smooth rolling texture of landform superimposed by coarse texture of trees and hedgerows to give even ballance. Rough pasture texture of fields + grass all year round.

LEVEL OF DIVERSITY [HOW MUCH - INCREASING, DECREASING, STATIC, - WHY - WITHIN LANDSCAPE UNIT / WITHIN TYPICAL COMPOSITION]
High level of diverisity of landform, vegetation, habitation, rocks, reservoir, stone walls, conifers etc. - static landscape.

CONTRIBUTORS TO GENIUS LOCI
Rock outcrops, small scale steep valleys, reservoir.

DEGREE OF UNITY [HOW MUCH IN THE LANDSCAPE UNIT. HOW MUCH IN A TYPICAL COMPOSITION / MAIN CONTRIBUTORS / DETRACTORS]
Unity in parcel as a whole - decrease will be slow - linked with gradual decline.

VISUAL TRAVEL [HOW THE EYE MOVES AROUND THE TYPICAL COMPOSITION]
Depends on viewing location - controlled by landform or vegetation. Generally along valleys, up hillsides to skyline. - Strongly enclosed.

BRIEF DESCRIPTION

An area of low intensity pastoral farming, still showing evidence of its proximity to urban areas, but also to upland areas with occasional walls and stone built farms/ cottages etc.

Urban influence reduced by strong density/strength of vegetation due to sheltered nature of valley landform. Steep winding sunken country lanes reinforce the nature of the valley landform and intimate nature of some parts of the unit. The reservoir is a developed tourist attraction as is the country park, and these areas have additional woodlands and distinctive character. In other areas tree cover tends to be reduced.

WOODLAND GUIDELINES
1) Woodland tied into existing vegetation pattern or responding to landform.
2) Internal shapes and mixtures need consideration because of ability to view across areas from opposite slopes.
3) Conifer + b/l.

PRINTED IN THE UK FOR HMSO Dd, 8373541, 7/93, C10, 38938